The Conversation Piece Collection

Paul Lowrie and
Bret Nicholaus

Ballantine Books New York

A Ballantine Book
Published by The Ballantine Publishing Group

http://www.randomhouse.com

Library of Congress Cataloging Card Number: 98-92891

ISBN: 0-345-91464-3

Text design by Beth Tondreau Design

Manufactured in the United States of America

First Edition: May 1998

10 9 8 7 6 5 4 3 2 1

Contents

BOOK ONE

The Conversation Piece

[Creative Questions to Tickle the Mind]

Dedicated to the life and memory of
Al Nicholaus

We'll meet again

Acknowledgments

Christina Nicholaus
Randy Bray
Joseph Durepos, literary agent

Thanks to our Heavenly Father,
who provides joy in all of life's journeys

Introduction

The book you are holding, *The Conversation Piece*, has been designed with you, the reader, in mind. Every question has been thoughtfully created to stimulate the most exciting conversation possible. All you have to do is read a question aloud and watch the fun begin.

There is no order to the questions, so you may randomly select any question in the book at any time. Of course, you may follow the questions in numerical order if you wish.

Some of the questions that follow you may have thought about but never discussed. Others will be brand-new to you. However, unlike some other books, ours does not contain questions regarding serious personal beliefs and ethics that can lead to tension and discomfort within a group. *The Conversation Piece* is a real opportunity for you and others to answer thought-provoking questions while still having *fun*.

After a question has been read, we suggest that persons be given approximately 60 seconds to consider their answers. Some questions may require more time for reflection, some may require less.

Since many of the questions are hypothetical in nature, you may not know exactly what you would do if the stated situation were actually to occur. That's all right! Simply give the answer that you *believe* at that moment would be your course of action. (Your answer may change from day to day.) Feel free to reword the question if it's not clear to you at first.

Above all, have a good time! Answer the questions honestly, but creatively. *Elaborate on your answers whenever possible.* If you can cover 20 questions, great! If one question leads to a 30-minute conversation, that's great, too! Remember that this book was designed to make your conversations more creative, interesting, and exciting.

So what are you waiting for? Gather some people together and start asking questions!

1

If you could fly in a hot-air balloon over any city in the world, what city would you choose?

2

Of all your favorite foods, which one would you find the most difficult to give up completely for the rest of your life?

3

You've been asked to design a zoological park for the future. How will you design this park to be radically different from the zoos of today? Be specific.

4

You've been given the chance to travel into the future to see how the world will change over the next 25 years. What change in particular are you most interested in?

5

While walking down a street in your neighborhood, you find a black briefcase clearly marked "Highly confidential information enclosed—do not open under any circumstances." What do you do?

6

More than likely, each of us has a favorite instrument, one whose sound we especially love. By the same token, we can probably name one instrument that we could easily do without. What instrument is *not* music to your ears?

7

Suppose you owned a large home in the country with a huge circular drive. If you could place any one thing in the center of that circle to greet your guests as they approached your home, what would it be?

8

What annually televised sporting event is an absolute must-see for you?

9

Suppose that each day you had to spend one hour in private meditation or contemplation and that by snapping your fingers, you could instantly transport yourself anywhere for the duration of this quiet time. Where would you choose to go?

10

How did they do that?! If you could learn the secret to any special effect or stunt from a popular movie, which one would you choose?

11

You're writing a mystery novel revolving around people who are disappearing one by one from a particular state in our country. The title, of course, is an important part of the success of the book. The catch: you must name the book after one of the 50 states (presumably, but not necessarily, the state from which the people are disappearing). Think marketing! Which state would you choose for the title of your book?

12

In your opinion, which animal is the most beautiful?

13

If you could be a part of any archeological dig, which one would it be?

14

If you were asked to make a "Top Ten" list of the people you regard as the all-time greatest Americans, whom would you rank first?

15

If you could have anything in the world completely to yourself for one day—any object or place—what would you choose?

16

If you were asked to design the ultimate treehouse for the kids in your neighborhood, what would you do to make the treehouse stand out?

17

If you could have any building or institution named after you, which one would you choose?

18

Coffee and donuts, ham and cheese—a couple of classic combinations. What food and/or beverage combination is your personal favorite?

19

Okay, TV viewers: What's your all-time favorite commercial jingle?

20

If, through the use of a time machine, you could venture to any point in time in the future, how many years down the road would you want to travel?

21

You've been asked to conceive of a way to make the sport of baseball more interesting to watch. You can change the rules, the playing surface, the makeup of the teams, whatever you want, but you can only make *one* change. What will it be?

22

If you could add one month to the calendar year, inserting it between two existing months, where would you put your extra 30 days?

23

If you could somehow control the weather and add an additional season to the year, what would your new season be like?

24

Suppose for a moment that you are *truly* color-blind: all you can see is black and white. Then one day you wake up to find you can now see *one* color. Which color would you wish it to be?

25

If a movie producer decided to do a movie about your life, in which genre—e.g., romance, comedy, adventure—would people more than likely find it?

26

If you had to choose one icon to serve as the national symbol for the word *kindness*, what would it be?

27

If you could play a one-on-one game against any NBA player, against whom would you most want to "take it to the hoop"?

28

If you could listen to only one type of music for one full year, what type of music would you choose?

29

If you could have any book instantly memorized—cover to cover—which book would you choose?

30

You've just been given the chance to host your own late-night talk show. You need good ratings to stay on the air. What will you do to make your show unique?

31

Suppose you won $50,000—but had to give it all away. To which charity, cause, or institution would you donate it?

32

Through the use of a time machine, you are traveling back to the year 1850. You may take with you one, and only one, product or invention from the modern era. What would you take with you to impress and awe our forebears?

33

If you could be anywhere in the world for New Year's Eve 1999, where would you most want to be?

34

What is the greatest lesson in life you've ever learned?

35

If you had to describe your disposition in meteorological terms, what would a typical forecast be? (Example: Partly sunny with the chance of a sudden thunderstorm.)

36

For many people, bridges conjure up thoughts of romance, serenity, and beauty. In all your travels, what is the most memorable bridge you've ever crossed?

37

Besides something considered immoral or politically controversial, what is something that, if you did it, would shock the socks off the people who know you? (Example: If you hate sports, attending a football game.)

38

If you could design the ultimate firework to conclude your city's Fourth of July display, what kind of explosion would it make?

39

If you could acquire a characteristic of one particular animal, what would it be?

40

If you were backed by investors to create, introduce, and market a new sport throughout the world, what would it be?

41

You've been taken into a canyon. There you must shout out any one sentence you choose. Through the use of advanced technology, your shout and its echo will be bottled and sold throughout the country, to be heard every time someone opens one of the bottles. What words will you shout?

42

If you joined the circus, what act would you most want to perform?

43

On a tour of the Alaskan wilderness, what would you want to see more than anything else?

44

What is your favorite number—one through nine—and why?

45

If you had to move to a new part of the country, would you want to move north, south, east, or west of where you live now?

46

Suppose that you are in charge of coordinating a parade for your city or town. Who would you choose as the grand marshal?

47

Which famous person do you imitate or impersonate best?

48

If you could erect a lighthouse that would guide all human beings toward one particular virtue, which virtue would it be?

49

If you could buy any rare collection in the world, which would you choose?

50

If you lived on a farm, which chore above all others would you definitely prefer *not* to do?

51

What do you believe is the greatest unsolved mystery of all?

52

If you had to rearrange the letters of your first name to give yourself a new name, what would it be?

53

What one word or phrase do you wish people would say more often?

54

In your opinion, what is the most beautiful man-made object?

55

If you could hear a speech from the leading figure in any field, who would you choose to hear?

56

On a scale of one to ten, with one being totally dishonest and ten being honest to the penny, how truthful would you be if someone asked you how much money you make in a year?

57

What aspect of your daily routine do you look forward to the most?

58

What is the longest walk you've ever taken?

59

If a sculptor were making a statue of you, in what position would you like to be rendered?

60

Which unwieldy item would you most like to see made portable?

61

In your opinion, what is the funniest looking animal?

62

If you could wake up tomorrow morning fluent in any language, which language would you choose?

63

If you could walk into any painting and actually experience the moment it depicts, which painting would you choose?

64

If the door to your home could be made in any shape other than a rectangle, what shape would you want it to be?

65

When you were a child, what job did you most want to have when you grew up?

66

In your opinion, what is the best piece of music, pop or classical, ever written?

67

If you were writing and producing an action-adventure movie, where would you film it?

68

If you could design the pattern of the coat of a new wild animal, what would it look like?

69

If you were an entry in the dictionary, under which word would people find you?

70

If you could change the custom of shaking hands, what would you replace it with?

71

If you could add any new course to our nation's school curriculum, what would it be?

72

You are given a magic potion that allows you to be invisible for one hour and one hour only. What would you want to do during your hour of invisibility?

73

A major motion picture is being made about your life. What song or songs should be on the soundtrack?

74

If you could have one superpower, what would you want it to be?

75

If you could see the front page of a national newspaper dated January 1, 2100, what do you imagine the main headline might say?

76

What would the title of your autobiography be (not including your name)?

77

If you owned a clock shop, to what time would you set the hands on the clock faces? (Assume the clocks are not running and that they all must show the same time.)

78

Which daily activity do you perform with the greatest care?

79

What would your dream house look like? Be descriptive!

80

What do you think is the best conversation piece in your home?

81

Which of the seven dwarfs personifies you best—Dopey, Sneezy, Sleepy, Bashful, Grumpy, Happy, or Doc?

82

If you could stand at the pinnacle of any natural object or man-made structure, what would it be?

83

If something other than a cuckoo could pop out of a clock to announce the time, what would you want it to be?

84

If you were sent on assignment to rate the ten best small towns in America, what particular criterion would be most important to you?

85

If you had to choose one flower to wear daily in your hair or on your lapel, which flower would it be?

86

If you could travel back in time to meet anyone in your family's history, whom would you most want to meet?

87

If you could have a large stained-glass window in your home, what would you want it to depict?

88

Which particular historical document (or portion thereof) do you think every American should know by heart?

89

The good ol' general store. What particular candy would you insist on finding in a big jar at the counter?

90

Which of the three daily meals do you look forward to the most?

91

If you owned a pickup truck, what item would you regularly lug around in it?

92

If you had to describe your personality using a Native American name, what would it be?

93

The year is 2050; having a grass lawn is a thing of the past. What might have replaced the green stuff?

94

What is something you forgot once that you will *never* forget again?

95

You're working on a national advertising campaign to get people to eat more fish. What will your campaign slogan be?

96

If you could domesticate any wild animal, which animal would it be?

97

If you could create a new piece of furniture for your home, one that is not available in any store, what would it be?

98

If you were writing a new children's book, what might you choose for the setting and who might the main character be?

99

If you were to issue a new postage stamp, who or what would be on it?

100

If you could start another fad along the lines of the Pet Rock craze of the late 1970s, what inanimate object would you choose as the new "pet"?

101

What is the longest line you've ever stood in?

102

If you could bottle something in nature and sell it, what would you choose?

103

We're all familiar with frequent flyer programs. Suppose there was a similar program to reward you for something else you do frequently in your life. What would it be?

104

If you could take a train ride across any of the seven continents, which continent would you choose?

105

Sometimes whistles blow to warn us or get our attention. When would you most like to have a whistle blow to alert you?

106

A picture is worth a thousand words. What is one place you have seen that only a picture can adequately describe?

107

If you could add a new room to your house, what would it be?

108

Assume that cars don't exist—you must travel everywhere on your bicycle. What special feature would you want that bike to have?

109

If you had to come up with a practical alternative to business cards, what would it be?

110

If you could bring back any retired sports star, living or deceased, to play in one game, who would it be?

111

As unrealistic as it may seem, consider for a moment an alternative to war. What else might nations do to settle their differences?

112

If you could add anything at all to an elevator ride to make it more interesting, what would it be?

113

If you had to be trapped in a TV show for a month, which show would you choose? Consider the setting, the characters, the lifestyle, and so on.

114

You must develop a brand-new course to be taught in colleges. What will it be?

115

What is one item you own that you really should throw away . . . but probably never will?

116

If you could change or eliminate one wedding tradition, what would it be?

117

If you could eliminate one month on the calendar, going directly from the month preceding it to the month following it, which month would it be?

118

What special feature that doesn't yet exist would you like to see added to automobiles?

119

Which of the following places do you think would be the most fun to live in: a tree, a cave, or an underground burrow? Use your imagination.

120

If you had lived in the Old West, what do you think your occupation would have been?

121

If you could take a boat cruise on any river in the world, which river would you choose?

122

If you could change the traditional meal of Thanksgiving from turkey to another food, what would you choose?

123

You've probably heard the expression "They couldn't pay me enough to do that job." What job would that be for you?

124

If the temperature *had* to be the same on every day of the year, what would you want it to be?

125

If you could open your own retail store, what type of merchandise would you sell?

126

Suppose you were attending a costume party tonight. What or whom would you want to be?

127

If you could play any instrument at the professional level, what instrument would it be?

128

If you could avoid one household chore the rest of your life, what chore would it be?

129

If you had to describe your personality in terms of a farm animal, which animal would you choose?

130

If you could have your picture taken with any living person in the world today, with whom would you choose to be photographed?

131

If you had to choose your own epitaph of seven words or less (besides name and dates), what would it be?

132

If any *one* of the national holidays had to be celebrated twice a year, which one would you want it to be?

133

Suppose you were in charge of designing a building for a large U.S. city. What would you do to distinguish your building from the others?

134

If you could take any scent and bottle it as a perfume or cologne, what scent would you choose?

135

If you could have 50 pounds of anything other than money, what would you want?

136

If you could teach a dog any new trick, what would it be?

137

With so many new products on the market, it is becoming increasingly difficult to "keep up with the Joneses." What item do you lack that leads you to believe that you have fallen *behind* the Joneses?

138

If you opened a restaurant, what would be your house specialty?

139

If you won a contest in which your prize was to select any three guests for *The Tonight Show*, which three people would you choose?

140

If you were given 20 acres of land and the money to develop it however you chose, what would you do with it?

141

What is your favorite day of the year?

142

If you were on an African safari, what would you absolutely have to see for your trip to be complete?

143

If everyone were required to wear a hat at all times, what sort of hat would you wear?

144

If money were not a consideration, what do you believe would be the ideal number of children to have?

145

What do you think is the most soothing sound?

146

If you could catch the ball to make the last out in the seventh game of the World Series, how would you want to make that play?

147

If you could take any job for just one month, what job would you like to have? (Assume that you would have the knowledge to perform adequately.)

148

If you could be one inch tall for a day, what specific place would you most like to explore?

149

If your picture could be on the cover of any magazine in America, on what magazine would you want to be pictured and what great accomplishment would put you there?

150

What, for you, would have been the most discouraging aspect of living in the 1800s?

151

If you were asked to create the ultimate vacation destination, what would it be like and where would it be located?

152

What truly daring or courageous feat would you like to witness in person?

153

If you could create a new Hollywood monster, what would your monster look like and what would it do?

154

You've no doubt seen little children having fun at the playground. Assuming good health, what would *you* most enjoy doing at a playground?

155

Suppose you were asked to redesign the American flag. What changes would you make?

156

If you were a mail carrier, what kind of weather would bother you the most?

157

If you could move the celebration of Christmas from December 25 to a new date, what day would you choose?

158

What is your favorite saying, quote, or expression?

159

If you were completely blind but could somehow see for one hour each week, how would you spend that time?

160

If you won $2 million in tomorrow's lottery, what is the biggest effect it would have on your life? Be specific.

161

What is something you have not yet done that you believe you can accomplish during your lifetime?

162

If you could enter a race horse in the Kentucky Derby, what would you name your horse?

163

You are going to the beach for the day. Besides your swimsuit, you may take only *one* other item along with you. What would it be?

164

If you were an artist, what would be the theme of your drawings/paintings?

165

If you could own another home in addition to the one(s) you already have, where would you want it to be?

166

Suppose you could have the ability to compete in any Olympic event. In what event would you want to compete?

167

Almost everyone has something that he/she considers a sure thing. What is your "ace in the hole"?

168

It is said that an apple a day keeps the doctor away. If you could select any food that, eaten every day, would keep the doctor away, what food would you choose?

169

What sound, other than ringing, would you like your telephone to make?

170

What would be the most enjoyable way for you to spend $25?

171

A visitor from abroad who has never been to the United States is coming to stay with you. What one place, attraction, or event would you be sure to take him or her to?

172

If it were commonplace for adults to play with children's toys, what toy would you most like to play with?

173

If you suddenly became a star and had to choose a stage name, what name would it be?

174

What task do you most often put off until tomorrow that you should do *today*?

175

If you could have been one of the early explorers of America, where would you have wanted to explore?

176

As the Christmas season approaches, what song is it that you just can't wait to hear?

177

What state in the Union would you be *least* interested in visiting?

178

What natural phenomenon or act of nature would you most like to see if you could witness it safely?

179

How would you redesign the dollar bill if you could?

180

If you could have "been there" to witness any specific moment in sports history, what moment would you choose?

181

What bit of knowledge/advice do you have that you wish you could pass on to everyone else?

182

What do you consider the ideal age to have a first child?

183

If sunset *had* to be at the same time every day of the year, what time would you want the sun to set?

184

What fear do you most want to be rid of forever?

185

Assume for a moment that your home is burning down. All the people and pets are safely outside and you have time to run back in to save *one* thing. What would you save?

186

If someone offered you a trip to any foreign country, where would you choose to visit?

187

Besides its intended purpose, what's the most creative way you can think of to use a paper clip?

188

If you could live anyone else's life for one month, *fully* experiencing their daily joys, sorrows, successes, and failures, whose life would you choose?

189

If you were given the money to build the world's greatest swimming pool, what would it be like?

190

If you and a partner had a free limousine at your disposal for one night, where would you most want to go?

191

If you could give any person a blue ribbon (other than a family member), to whom would you give it and why?

192

What event in American history that occurred during your lifetime do you most vividly remember?

193

If you were given 1,000 fresh roses, what would you do with them?

194

If you could take a "behind the scenes" look at anything, what would you most want to see?

195

What would be the ideal way for you to spend a hot Saturday afternoon in the middle of July?

196

If you could go back in time to witness any invention or discovery, what would you choose to see?

197

What's your favorite food to order when you eat at an upscale restaurant?

198

If you could channel your frustration whenever you became angry into any nondestructive activity, what would you choose to do?

199

Suppose you could eliminate television commercials but still had to fill the time slots. What would you choose to replace the commercials?

200

If you had a parrot and could teach it to say any word or short phrase, what would it be?

201

If *you* could set the hours of your 40-hour workweek, how would you distribute the time?

202

If you were an airline pilot and were told to choose any route that you would have to fly for your entire career, what two cities would your flight connect?

203

If you could see to it that one magazine was on every coffee table in America, what magazine would you choose?

204

If you could be any age again for one week, what age would you be?

205

Which of the four seasons do you most anticipate?

206

If you were to write a book, what would you choose as the topic?

207

If you could go back in time to safely witness any battle in world history, which battle would you choose to see?

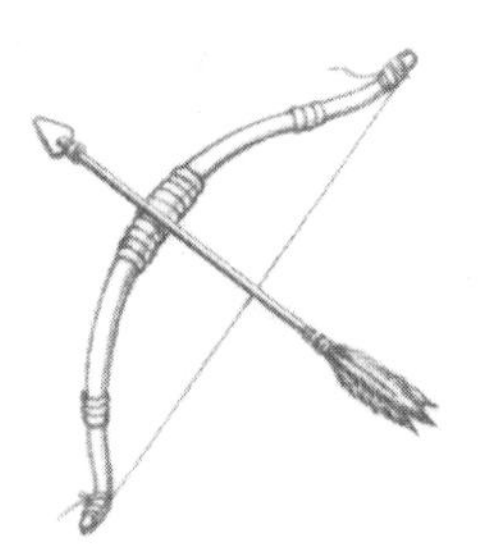

208

Everyone at work has been asked to place an ornament on the company Christmas tree that best represents him/herself. What would *your* ornament look like?

209

What is one event in the future whose outcome you would like to know *now*?

210

If you could have two front-row tickets to see any singer or musical group, whose concert would you attend?

211

If you were asked to create the ultimate dessert, what would it be?

212

If you could proclaim a new national holiday, what would it be and how would we celebrate it?

213

What is something that you enjoy that is a chore for most other people?

214

You must choose a movie to show at a party attended by many adults from different backgrounds and lifestyles. What movie would you choose to show?

215

What world record would you most want to establish?

216

If you could invite anyone in the world to your house for dinner, whom would you invite and what would you serve them?

217

You must bury a time capsule to be opened 200 years from now. What three items would you put in the capsule to give people an idea of life in the 1990s?

218

What particular sound annoys you the most?

219

What animal would you most like to house in your backyard, if you could?

220

You can design any new ride or attraction for Walt Disney World. What will it be?

221

What is an item that you own that has a minimal monetary value but has such sentimental value that you would not sell it for $5,000?

222

On a scale of one to ten (with one being very uneasy and ten being very comfortable), how comfortable would you feel delivering a 15-minute speech to an audience of 200 people?

223

If you could be the spokesperson for any product on the market, what product would you choose to represent?

224

What is the most exciting event you've ever witnessed?

225

If you had to substitute-teach for two months, which grade (kindergarten through twelfth) would you choose to teach?

226

If you had one hour each day to relax *completely*, what would you want to do for that hour?

227

What object, place, or attraction would you classify as the greatest "wonder of the world"?

228

If it were socially acceptable for you to dress for work any way you liked, what would be your typical outfit?

229

If you owned a yacht, what would you name it?

230

If you could be remembered for any act of bravery, what would it be?

231

If you could be any inanimate object for a day, what would you be?

232

If you could be "home for the holidays" with family and friends anywhere in the world, where would you want to be?

233

Which month of the year do you *least* anticipate?

234

What "moment of glory" have you watched another person celebrate that you too would love to experience?

235

What do you consider the ideal household income for a family of four?

236

At what local, regional, or national event would hearing "The Star-Spangled Banner" be most meaningful for you?

237

If drinking fountains could dispense another liquid, what would you want it to be?

238

What is the most interesting course you have ever taken in school?

239

If you could appear as a guest star on any television show, which show would you choose?

240

If you had only enough time each day to read *one* section of the newspaper, which section would you choose to read?

241

If you could go back in time and somehow avert any tragedy in American history, what incident would you choose to prevent?

242

If you were chosen to be a participant in the Rose Bowl Parade simply because of who you are, in what type of vehicle would you most like to ride?

243

If you had $15 to spend at the ballpark, how would you spend it? (Assume you would not have to pay for your ticket or parking.)

244

If you were a migrating bird, where would you fly for the winter?

245

Everyone hears discussions that they consider boring. What topic can put *you* to sleep more quickly than any other?

246

What item that you don't currently possess would you most like to have in your home?

247

If you could have a memento of any famous person, what would you want it to be?

248

Besides the usual horse and dog races, what type of animal race do you think would be interesting to watch? (Assume the animals would be treated well.)

249

Which food would you rank first on you list of *least* favorite foods?

250

The U.S. government has asked you to pick another animal in addition to the eagle to depict America. What animal would you choose?

251

If you could have a window view from your office in a 100-story building, what floor would you want to be on?

252

If you were completely deaf but were somehow able to hear for one hour each week, what would you want to hear for that hour?

253

If Christmas were tomorrow, what gift would you want most?

254

On a scale of one to ten (with one being very comfortable and ten being very uneasy), how uneasy would you feel sitting between two strangers on an airplane?

255

If you *had* to change your first name, what would you choose as your new name?

256

If you had to wear a button with a maximum of five words on it describing your outlook on life, what would your button say?

257

In a spelling bee, what word would you hope you would *not* have to spell?

258

What specific aspect of being a child do you miss the most?

259

What is the most beautiful drive you've ever taken? Be as descriptive as possible.

260

Of all the movie *characters* you've seen, which one do you believe is most like you?

261

What, for you, would have been the most exciting aspect of living in the preceding century? Be specific.

262

What do you believe the fine should be for running a red light? Assume the light has been red for several seconds.

263

What outdoor scent do you enjoy more than any other?

264

For a literally sensational experience, you have been offered the chance to jump off a diving board into a pool filled with *anything* of your choice. Into what substance would you want to jump?

265

Suppose your dream NBA Championship or Super Bowl could be realized. What two teams would be playing each other and which team would you root for?

266

If you were given an unlimited amount of money and the necessary technology to invent anything you desired, what would you invent?

267

What specific subject do you feel you know better than any other subject?

268

You are walking alone at night on a suburban street when a man wearing a black mask confronts you and demands your money. It does not appear that he is carrying a weapon, but you do not know for certain. How do you respond?

269

If you could create and market a toothpaste in any flavor besides mint, what new flavor would you choose?

270

Suppose you could be on vacation with pay for the entire summer. Also assume that someone offered to pay for any summer adventure you could imagine. Where would you choose to go and what would you do?

271

If you were given a $50 gift certificate to spend in any store, where would you choose to redeem it?

272

What thought or sentiment would you like to put in one million fortune cookies?

273

What is one of the simple pleasures of life you truly enjoy?

274

If you could invent a pair of glasses that would allow you to see abstract things (e.g., the motives behind someone's actions), what would you want to see?

275

As a form of punishment, children are sometimes deprived temporarily of something they cherish. If you were going to be punished in this way as an adult, what item would you least want to lose? (Assume the deprivation would last one month.)

276

What is something that most people consider a modern-day convenience that you consider a pain in the neck?

277

If you could break or smash any object against a brick wall whenever you needed to release frustration, what object would you choose?

278

If you were invited to a dinner party, what hors d'oeuvre would you most want to find on the table?

279

If you had a great voice and were given a contract to record an album, what style of music would you sing?

280

Suppose you lived in a house surrounded by acres of trees. What particular type of tree would you want flourishing on your land?

281

You've seen signs that say No Smoking, No Pets, No Trespassing, etc. If you could put an original "No ____ " sign on your front door, what would it say?

282

If you could have a scale model of anything you wanted, what would it be?

283

If you could speak for one minute by phone to anyone living in the world, who would it be?

284

If you could go to a land of make-believe for one day, what would you most want to experience?

285

If you could own a sweatshirt that advertised any place in the world, what would it promote?

286

Most people have a story or experience that they love to share with other people. Here's your chance. What's *your* story?

287

If you could be one of America's "most wanted," but wanted because of some *skill* you have, what great skill would you want to possess?

288

How much money would a person have to pay you to spend one night alone in an old mansion that is supposedly haunted?

289

If you could find out only *one* fact about every person you met, what fact would you want to know?

290

If neither time nor money were an issue, what do you think would be the most enjoyable way to travel from New York to California?

291

If you could have the *original* of anything, what would you want it to be?

292

If you could carve your name in stone anywhere in America, where would you do it?

293

If you had a personal maid or butler who would perform only *one* task a day for you, what job would you choose to have her/him do?

294

If you were given $2,000 to put toward anything of your choice, how would you spend the money?

295

If you could go back in time and live through any five-year period in history, what period would you choose?

296

When you consider nature and/or creation, what do you stand most in awe of?

297

In what field of endeavor would you most want to take a two-hour crash course?

298

What would an island paradise be like for you? Describe it in detail.

299

If you *really* wanted to upset your dentist, what would you eat immediately before having your teeth cleaned?

300

If, like a product, your behavior came with a guarantee, what could you *honestly* guarantee about yourself?

301

If you were told that you could watch only *one* television show a week for one year, what show would you choose to watch?

302

Which sport would you most like to play professionally?

303

If you could create a memorial to yourself in a city park, what would it be?

304

If you were a member of a national public relations staff, what spectacular event would you like to stage in celebration of the Fourth of July?

305

If you could go back in time and relive any moment in your life exactly as it originally happened, what event would you choose to experience again?

306

You have two choices:

1. You may live in a region where the day and nighttime temperature is always between 80 and 90 degrees Fahrenheit, or . . .

2. You may live in a region where the day and nighttime temperature is always between 40 and 50 degrees Fahrenheit.

Which would you choose?

307

If you could write a sequel to any movie, what movie would it be?

308

If you had to have the same topping on your vanilla ice cream for the rest of your life, what topping would you choose?

309

By how many hours would you lengthen the 24-hour day to allow yourself enough time to do everything you need to do?

310

If you were asked to create the ultimate candy bar, what would it be like?

311

You are offered an envelope that you know contains $50. You are then told that you may either keep it or exchange it for another envelope that *may* contain $500 or *may* be empty. Do you keep the first envelope or do you take your chances with the second?

312

If you could wake up every morning and look out your bedroom window at the perfect view, what would that view be?

313

If you were offered a 60-second spot during prime-time television to say or promote anything you wanted, how would you use this time?

314

Assume that you are stranded for one month on an uninhabited tropical island that *does* have shelter and plenty of food and water. What one item would you want with you on the island?

315

What national attraction or tourist site should every American see at least once?

316

If you could go back in time and ask any famous person in history one question, whom would you question and what would you ask? (Assume you would be given an honest answer.)

317

If you could experience something considered very dangerous with your safety guaranteed, what would you want to experience?

318

Almost everyone can recall a missed photo opportunity because he/she did not have a camera. What moment above all others do you wish you could have caught on film?

319

On a scale of one to ten (with one being very relaxing and ten being very stressful), how stressful is your job?

320

If you could add any question to this book, what would it be?

BOOK TWO

The Mom & Dad Conversation Piece

[Creative Questions to Celebrate the Family]

To my mom and late dad, for their unceasing support, immeasurable self-sacrifice, and limitless love!

To my wife and best friend, Christina, for saying "yes" to the most important question I've ever asked her.

—Bret Nicholaus

To my mom and dad for their unending love.

—Paul Lowrie

Mutual thanks:

To Joseph Purepos, literary agent, his wife, Betty, and our friend, Randy Bray, for their help on this project.

To our Lord Jesus Christ, who guides us daily through the greatest commandment: "Love the Lord your God with all your heart and with all your soul and with all your mind," and secondly, "Love your neighbor as yourself." (Mathew 22:37–40).

Welcome

. . . to moms, dads, sons, and daughters everywhere

Whether you own the title of mom or dad for yourself or have a mom or dad (or both) that you care about and love, you'll find this collection of questions to be a wonderful keepsake that can be enjoyed and cherished forever. While we all, predictably, know much about our own moms and dads, there are some things that we've never asked—but would love to know. And there are many things that our parents would love to share—but have never told. This book gives moms and dads the opportunity to share favorite childhood memories, family values, vacation experiences, and words of wisdom they hope will be followed even after they're gone; it also encourages parents of all ages to share their most exciting moments in life, as well as the dreams and aspirations they still hold for the future.

In today's fast-paced world, the art of conversation —and certainly the sharing of ourselves with others— seems to have diminished. This book of questions allows conversation to take on a whole new meaning—one that appropriately benefits parents as well as children. Mom can share those important aspects of life that she wants to impart to her children; Dad can pass along the thoughts that he deems significant; and children (young or old) will be able to more fully appreciate who their parents are. Though many of the questions go well beyond typical triviality, you'll find that there is always an entertaining quality about the questions—and that even the most thought-provoking queries are *positive* in nature.

Because of the fun, entertaining style of the questions, moms or dads buying this book for family use will find that even young children will be interested in the answers, not to mention the questions themselves. If you are an adult giving this book to your mom or dad, you know how valuable their thoughts and experiences in life can be and will find that these questions will enrich your conversations with them.

Keep in mind that this book can be enjoyed with friends as easily as with family members, since it provides as many good laughs as it does opportunities for serious contemplation. Then again, you may decide simply to read the questions to yourself as you reflect on your life and that of your children. (Just because the word *conversation* appears in the title doesn't mean this book can't be experienced equally well in the silence of your own bedroom!) *We do encourage moms and dads to consider writing down their answers; this will provide a priceless keepsake for your children.* However you decide to enjoy the book, make sure you do just that—enjoy it! And may we find as sons and daughters—or as moms and dads—that parents truly are treasure chests of insights, memories, and inspiration; we need only give them the chance to open up to us!

1

For each of your children, where were you and what were you doing when you realized that it was definitely time for your baby to be born?

2

When you were growing up, what was dinnertime like in your home? What was a typical meal?

3

What are some of the very first things you can remember teaching your children to do?

4

When did your dad or mom first let you get behind the wheel of the car? What was your most interesting experience when you were learning to drive?

5

Who is the most famous person you've ever met face-to-face?

6

What is something you and your spouse have always done together that many couples would consider trite and boring, but that the two of you find very meaningful?

7

Who was your best friend in high school? What made you and your friend so compatible?

8

What is the greatest lesson your children have ever taught you?

9

As a child, what was your favorite family tradition?

10

As a parent, what family tradition is or was the most meaningful for you?

11

What was your first car? What one feature above all others made it special to you?

12

If you could go back to the beginning and start over, what particular job or career do you think you would've really enjoyed pursuing?

13

What trip above all others do you think is best enjoyed when taken by car?

14

If a tree were going to be planted in your honor—or, ultimately, in your memory—what type of tree would you want it to be?

15

Virtually everyone remembers what he or she was doing when the news came. Where were you and what were you doing when you learned of the John F. Kennedy assassination?

16

When you were growing up, what was the most memorable family vacation you ever took?

17

As a mom or dad yourself, what has been the most memorable vacation you and your children have taken?

18

If you could pass down one and only one—family recipe to your children, which recipe would you choose?

19

We're used to describing ourselves in terms of height, hair color, and eye color; but how would you describe your *smile* to someone? Be as detailed as you can.

20

Whose party (birthday, anniversary, retirement, and the like) above all others will you never forget?

21

What is one childlike quality that you have maintained throughout your life?

22

With respect to raising your children, what is your greatest accomplishment?

23

Who is one friend from yesteryear whom you've completely lost contact with, but with whom you would love to somehow reestablish ties?

24

What is your favorite wedding-day memory?

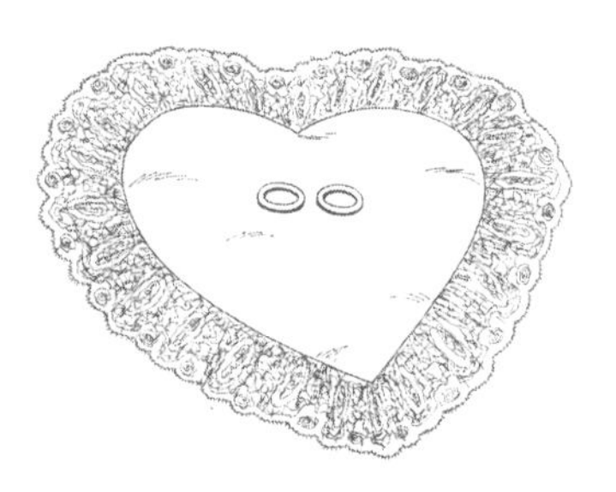

25

What daily time or activity do you treasure more than any other?

26

Clothing trends and styles come and go, but each of us has a favorite. What has been your favorite clothing trend/style over the years?

27

Why did you choose the names that you did for your children? How easy was it to decide on the names?

28

What particular childhood Christmas memory do you remember most fondly?

29

What particular Christmas memory as a parent do you treasure the most?

30

If you could choose only one famous quote that you would want your children to always remember, which one would it be?

31

What was your favorite record to listen to growing up?

32

What TV mom or dad do you think you are most similar to?

33

When you were growing up, what did you get into trouble for more often than anything else?

34

Which of your birthdays did you anticipate with the greatest joy?

35

Each of us can probably name an age we *didn't* want to turn. What birthday were you the least enthusiastic to celebrate at the time?

36

What is the most daring feat you've ever accomplished (or tried to accomplish) during your lifetime?

37

If you were asked to choose the "family movie of the decade," what film would get your top vote?

38

What is one family vacation you have never taken but would still love to take someday?

39

What specific thing was the most enjoyable for you to teach your children?

40

If money were not a concern, what do you believe would be the ideal number of children to have?

41

Virtually everyone can recall a household accident like falling off a ladder. What is your most interesting mishap at home?

42

If you were allowed to keep only one family photograph, which one would you choose? How old are the children in this picture?

43

If you could add one room onto the house that would serve any unique purpose you desired, what would the room be?

44

In your opinion, what quality above all others is essential to instill in children today?

45

We're all experts at something (if only in our own minds). What particular topic do you believe you know well enough that you could at least entertain the thought of writing a book about it?

46

What is your favorite song of all time?

47

What was the most exciting sports moment you ever witnessed?

48

What has been the best five-year period of your life thus far?

49

What toy from your childhood did you treasure above all others?

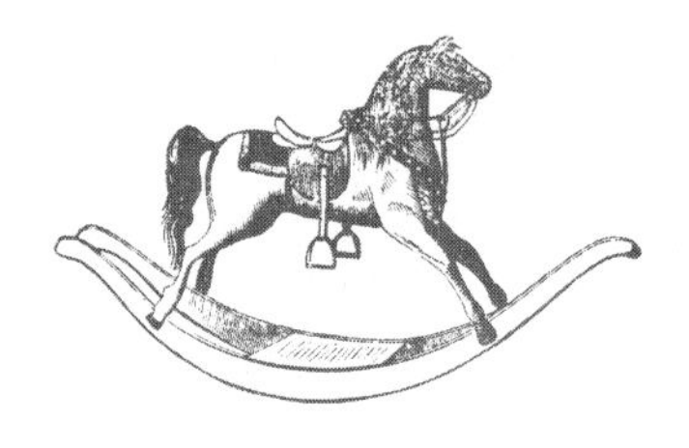

50

Besides a spouse or a child, what has been the greatest blessing in your life?

51

What one article of clothing (besides a wedding dress) will you probably always hold on to because of its sentimental value?

52

What activity or event above all others do you think every family should experience together at least once?

53

Besides a family member, which person (living or deceased) has had the greatest influence on your becoming the person you are today?

54

Besides a family member, is there any person whose life you feel you've in some way made better?

55

What is the greatest book you've ever read?

56

In your opinion, what would be the ideal place (city, state, geographic location, and the like) in which to raise a family?

57

What is the best clean joke you've ever heard?

58

If you could have a one-hour conversation with any person in your family's history, whom would you choose? What specific questions would you ask of him or her?

59

If you had the chance to take another honeymoon, where would you most want to go?

60

What was the most unusual hairstyle you ever had?

61

In general, at what age do you think children are the cutest to observe?

62

In the classroom of life, what lesson do you believe we must continuously try to master day after day?

63

If you had to pick one particular aspect that makes a house a home, what would it be?

64

As a child, what was the first "business" venture you ever undertook? (Example: A lemonade stand.)

65

If you had more time on your hands, what hobby would you most like to pursue diligently?

66

What is the oldest keepsake in your possession?

67

In your opinion, what is the secret of life?

68

What is the greatest goal you want to achieve within the next five years?

69

What has been your greatest personal accomplishment in life?

70

What faraway friends whom you seldom get to see anymore do you wish you could visit more frequently?

71

Who was your favorite actor or actress when you were a teenager? Who is your all-time favorite actor or actress?

72

With respect to your spouse, when or how did you know that you were truly in love?

73

What were the very first fully understandable words that your baby spoke?

74

You should never measure a person's success by the size of his or her wallet. How do *you* measure a person's success in life?

75

What particular Father's Day and/or Mother's Day do you remember the most?

76

Besides the actual birth of your children, what has been your proudest moment as a mom or dad?

77

Someday, when the pressures of raising a family are well behind you, you may actually find time to start writing the Great American Novel. As the author, what would you choose for the setting and the plot?

78

What is the most important thing that your parents did in raising you that you also did—or are doing—in raising *your* children?

79

What is the oldest photograph you have of someone in your family's history?

80

If you had the power to solve one—and only one—problem in the world today, what problem would you eradicate?

81

Suppose that you were asked to make a 15-minute videotape of yourself that would give your children something to remember you by when you're deceased. Assuming that this will be the only video of you available to your children, what would you want to be doing on the tape?

82

What was the weather like on the day you got married?

83

Suppose you could combine the personalities and attributes of any three people in history to create the consummate mom or dad. Which three people would you choose?

84

What is the best birthday gift you can remember receiving?

85

For today's teens, the local mall seems to be the popular spot to rendezvous. Where was your favorite spot to "hang out" when you were a teenager?

86

As a mom, what do you think is the most difficult aspect of being a dad in today's world?

87

As a dad, what do you think is the most difficult aspect of being a mom in today's world?

88

Besides something directly related to the family (i.e., the birth of a child), what has been the most exciting day of your life?

89

Many people carry something they treasure in their wallet. Besides a picture of family members, is there any really meaningful item that you keep with you in your wallet?

90

Where did you get engaged? How was the marriage proposal made?

91

What one Scripture verse or other powerful instruction for living do you hope your children will always remember?

92

What was one negative in your life that you were somehow able to turn into something quite positive?

93

If you were writing your memoirs today, what would be the most appropriate title?

94

Besides hugs and kisses, what do you believe is the best way to show your children that you really love them?

95

If you were making a list of your three favorite childhood memories, what would the entries be?

96

What is something that most parents would consider a chore that you actually enjoy (or have enjoyed) doing?

97

What is the kindest thing a stranger has ever done for you?

98

In your opinion, what has been the biggest news event (national or international) during your lifetime?

99

What was your favorite household scent as a child?

100

Over the course of your life, what would you say has been your favorite room in the house?

101

What were your parents' most distinguishing physical features?

102

What is something memorable that you once saw or did that your children will probably never have the opportunity to see or experience? (Example: Talking to a veteran of World War I.)

103

Dads (or moms): What is your favorite food to throw on the grill?

104

Moms (or dads): What is your favorite item to bake?

105

If you could relive one full year of your life exactly as it originally happened, to what year would you return?

106

Suppose that a movie were going to be made about your life. Who do you think would be best suited to play you in the film?

107

If you had to describe your disposition in terms of a musical instrument, which one would you choose?

108

Is there anyone you know of in your family's history who had an encounter with or knew someone famous?

109

What was your favorite grade in school?

110

What do you remember most about your first Christmas as a mom or dad?

111

Most moms and dads have at one time or another taken something away from a child as an appropriate form of punishment. If a child were going to similarly punish you as an adult for doing something wrong, what would you find most difficult to give up?

112

Thanksgiving and Christmas seem to get all the credit when it comes to memorable holidays. So . . . what was a typical Fourth of July celebration like for you when you were a child?

113

Suppose that you were asked to sketch out on paper your family tree. What type of tree would represent your family? Be creative!

114

When you have bad days, what is the best thing you can do to make yourself happy again?

115

If you could pass along only one piece of advice on how to feel fulfillment in life, what would you say?

116

What are your three all-time greatest memories as a parent?

117

What is the silliest, most off-the-wall thing you've ever done in your life?

118

What word or short phrase do you think more people need to say more often?

119

As a young child, what was your favorite children's book to read?

120

What has been the most enjoyable club, league, or team to which you have ever belonged?

121

What is something you've always wished you could do well, but as yet have not been able to master?

122

Kids do say the darnedest things! What is something your child once said at a young age that you'll never forget?

123

Besides eating right and exercising, what do you believe is the key to living a healthy life?

124

What one topic above all others do you believe a person should avoid discussing with other people?

125

Everyone has a purpose for being here. What have you come to see as your place in this world?

126

What is the best piece of advice you've ever received?

127

What is the best piece of advice you've ever given to your children?

128

Excluding any family members, which particular person whom you know do you have the most respect for?

129

If you had to pick one thing that every boy should have while growing up, what would it be?

130

If you had to pick one thing that every girl should have while growing up, what would it be?

131

If you were attending a large party where you didn't know any of the guests, what type of person (in terms of personality, lifestyle, etc.) would you be most prone to seek out?

132

What is the best class you've ever taken in your life?

133

In terms of mannerisms or physical appearance, have you ever been compared to a famous person? If so, whom?

134

Which of life's mysteries are you most curious about?

135

What is the highest honor or award you've ever received in your life?

136

In your opinion, what is the ideal age to become a parent?

137

What is the most memorable family outing you've ever taken with your children?

138

Just for fun, have you ever added up how much money you've earned to this point in your life?

139

What is the very first thing that you can clearly remember from your childhood?

140

Suppose that all the cards from a standard deck were lying faceup in front of you on a table. If you had to pick 1 of the 52 cards to abstractly represent your life, which card would you choose?

141

In terms of numbers, what is the largest Thanksgiving Day celebration you've ever been a part of?

142

What is your most memorable Thanksgiving Day experience?

143

Which particular attribute of your own mom do you see the most in yourself?

144

Which particular attribute of your own dad do you see the most in yourself?

145

What would you list as the three most memorable TV moments you've ever seen?

146

What professional athlete or otherwise famous person do you believe is the best role model for children today?

147

What famous person (living or deceased) do you think every adult would do well to try and emulate?

148

What were the big events going on in the world the year you were born? Who was president?

149

What would you choose as the greatest accomplishment or development in the world during your lifetime?

150

When you meet people for the first time, what are you generally the most interested in learning about them?

151

What was your first full-time job? Do you remember what your hourly pay was?

152

What is the most valuable fact or insight that you have learned during the past year?

153

What is the most memorable road you've ever driven on?

154

Over the course of your life, what activity has most consistently given you a feeling of inner peace?

155

As a child, who was your hero (fictitious or real)?

156

If you had more time in the day, what would you spend it doing?

157

As far as you know, who in your family's history has lived the longest?

158

Besides, quite obviously, being in love, what do you think is the key to a successful marriage?

159

As a youngster, whose house did you always look forward to visiting?

160

If you had to give yourself an appropriate sobriquet (Abraham Lincoln's was "Honest Abe"), what would it be?

161

During your life, have you ever celebrated your birthday the same day that a major news event was occurring?

162

Suppose that three objects that you own were going to be buried in a time capsule to be opened by future family members 100 years from now. What three objects would give them the most valuable insight as to who you were as a person?

163

If you could leave your loved ones only three instructions to get them through life successfully, which three would you choose?

164

In your opinion, what is the greatest comfort of home—tangible or intangible?

165

Do you generally live your life for the present or for the future?

166

What one thing above all others did you really dislike as a child that you have come to fully appreciate as an adult?

167

Allowing for exceptions to the rule, what is something you truly believe dads will always be better at than moms when it comes to raising kids?

168

Allowing for exceptions to the rule, what is something you truly believe moms will always be better at than dads when it comes to raising kids?

169

In your opinion, what has been the biggest change in the way people think or act since your childhood?

170

What is the longest project you've ever worked on?

171

Where have the best times of your life taken place?

172

With what famous person's life story do you think every adult should be familiar?

173

If you had to make a "Top Ten" list of people you've met over the years who represent the best that humankind has to offer, who would make this elite list?

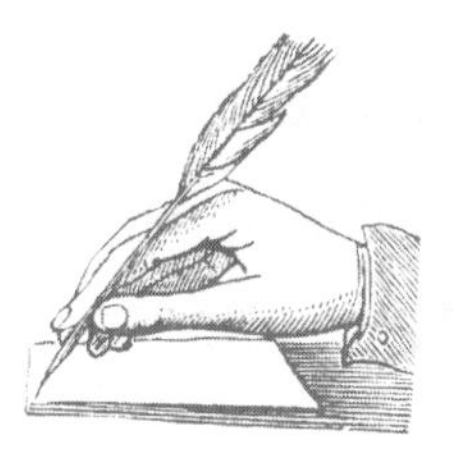

174

What's the best gift you ever received from your children?

175

What is the most interesting thing that happened on your honeymoon?

176

What event/occurrence in your past changed your life for the better more than any other?

177

As a mom or dad with older children, what is your favorite thing to do with your son or daughter?

178

As a mom or dad with younger children, what was—or is—your favorite activity to do with your son or daughter?

179

What was the most mischievous thing you can recall doing as a young child?

180

If you had had another baby girl, what would you have been likely to name her?

181

If you had had another baby boy, what might you have chosen as his name?

182

Suppose that each family in the neighborhood had to put a Christmas ornament on the town tree. Assuming that the ornament was supposed to represent your family's ideals, what would it look like?

183

As a parent, what were your thoughts the first day your child went off to kindergarten?

184

Do you have any recollections of your *own* days in kindergarten?

185

When you were a very young child, what did you want to be when you grew up? When you were in high school, what did you think you would be doing for a living someday?

186

What is one family tradition that you have not yet experienced but would love to start?

187

When you think of your hometown, what image pops into your mind first?

188

In children's bedrooms today—especially teenagers' rooms—one is likely to find posters or pictures tacked to the walls. What did your bedroom walls, dressers, and the like display as a teenager?

189

Did your mom and dad have favorite expressions they would always say? If so, what were they?

190

What fad can you remember *really* getting into as a child? Any favorite fads as an adult?

191

Every family has at least one element that makes it truly unique. What was one of the more unique aspects of your family when you were growing up?

192

What is one of the unique aspects of your own family today?

193

Assume for a moment that you could actually decide exactly how you want to look (i.e., physical characteristics). In an ideal world, how would you look? Be as specific as you can.

194

When you turn your thoughts to your children, what makes you the most proud?

195

As a child, what was your favorite pet?

196

Almost all of us wish our lives could be more relaxing and simplified. If you could use only three key words, how would you best describe "the simple life" as you wish it could be?

197

What was the first "big" item that you bought after you were married?

198

What is one buzzword or phrase that was highly popular during your teenage years?

199

What was your favorite game to play as a child? What's your all-time favorite game as an adult?

200

Regardless of what was going on in your personal life, what year during your lifetime would you have liked to have been stuck in, yourself aging at a normal rate, but with society basically staying the same forever after?

201

How many different states have your ancestors lived in?

202

What is the earliest lesson you can remember learning as a child that you have followed throughout your life?

203

If you could've been born in any year before or after the year you were *actually* born, what year would you choose?

204

In your opinion, what would have been the ideal time of year (month and date) for you to have been born?

205

How old were you when you went on your very first date? Where did you go?

206

Did you ever have a special hiding place as a child?

207

What was your favorite summertime activity when you were growing up?

208

Approximately how many students were in your high school graduating class?

209

If 20 people who know you were asked to describe you using only one adjective, what do you think would be the most popular word used?

210

When did your children take their first baby steps?

211

What is the most memorable phone call you've ever received?

212

Walt Disney, no stranger to tough times, once said, "I think it's important to have a good hard failure when you're young." Do you agree or disagree with his statement? Why?

213

What is the greatest distance you've ever traveled by car for a family vacation?

214

When you think of all the photographs you've taken on your family vacations, which one comes to mind first?

215

As a child, what did you wish for more often and/or more sincerely than anything else?

216

Mom: Besides physical appearance, which of Dad's qualities/personality traits initially attracted you to him?

217

Dad: Besides physical appearance, which of Mom's qualities/personality traits initially attracted you to her?

218

Can you recall a particular brand name that was extremely trendy during your teenage years?

219

Many young people today hear about the past and can't imagine life without some of today's conveniences. What is one modern-day convenience that you didn't have when growing up that, quite honestly, was easy to live without?

220

What is something you were initially reluctant to let your children have or do, but to which you ultimately acquiesced after much pleading and begging on their part?

221

What is the most memorable walk you've ever taken?

222

What is the most important text (or portion of text) you've ever memorized during your life?

223

When you look back on the life you've lived to this point, what amazes you the most?

224

What is one item you got rid of years ago that you wish you could have back?

225

When you were 16 years old, what do you remember being able to buy for one dollar?

226

What is the greatest leap of faith you've ever taken?

227

What was the most exciting event or occurrence that ever took place in your hometown?

228

Moms: What is something you truly appreciate or enjoy doing that most women probably don't care for?

229

Dads: What is something you truly appreciate or enjoy doing that most men probably don't care for?

230

In your opinion, what is the highest compliment anyone can receive?

231

Between fixing the home and fixing dinner, moms' and dads' hands are often full—literally! Over the years, with which tool, implement, or utensil have you felt the most at ease?

232

Over the course of your life, what have you probably spent more time pondering than anything else?

233

Suppose that upon your death a memorial fund were established in your name and that a substantial amount of money was received. For what purpose or cause would you want the money to be used?

234

Even though you probably weren't of any *real* assistance, with which household job did you love to help your mom or dad when you were a child?

235

What is the most romantic thing your spouse has ever done for you?

236

What was the address of your very first residence (i.e., your parents' address when you were born)?

237

Above everything else, what one thing do you personally believe all people should do or experience at least once in their lifetime—just to say they've done it?

238

What is your most interesting family-reunion memory?

239

During your first year or two of marriage, what illusion did you have about married life that you soon came to realize wasn't true?

240

"Knock on wood." Which aspect of your life thus far has luck generally seemed to favor?

241

Besides your own mom or dad, which family member (grandma, grandpa, aunt, uncle, etc.) do you think you physically resemble the most?

242

In what ways do you believe life is analogous to each of the following geographical features: a mountain, a river, and an open plain? Be creative, yet honest.

243

Before any of your children were actually born, how many children did you envision yourself having and what sex did you want them to be?

244

If you had to choose one thing you own that has more sentimental value than any other, what object would you pick?

245

If you could have a professional photograph taken of your family anywhere in the world (presumably somewhere from which a family photo doesn't already exist), where would you want the picture taken?

246

Of all the American presidents during your lifetime, which one has been your favorite?

247

What is the greatest compliment you've ever been paid?

248

If your life were literally flashing before your eyes, what are five moments or scenes that you would expect to stand out?

249

What one place above all others do you like to go to when you need peace, quiet, and time for reflection?

250

At some point in your life, you no doubt knew someone who did something for you, seemingly insignificant at the time, that ultimately had a profound impact on the direction your life took (personally or professionally). Who was it, what did he or she do, and how has it affected your life?

251

In terms of the big picture, what surprises you most about life? (Example: Its brevity.)

252

Looking back to when you were 21 years old, what was your biggest misconception about how your own future would unfold?

253

Moms: If you could receive a bouquet consisting of three different kinds of flowers, which three would you want in the arrangement?

254

Dads: What is (or was) your favorite tie? Did you ever wear a tie you didn't like simply because your child gave it to you as a gift?

255

Did you ever do anything for your children that you *never* would have done for anyone else?

256

If you could choose only one question and corresponding answer from this book for your children to always remember, which one would it be?

BOOK THREE

The Christmas Conversation Piece

[Creative Questions to Illuminate the Holidays]

This book is dedicated to the following people:

My wife and best friend, Christina, for her constant love.

My mom, Lorrie, who always, *always* made the house a home and who taught me more about how to live than she'll ever know.

My late dad, Alan, and my late grandfathers, David Raymond Johnson and Herbert Nicholaus, all three of whom were loved and respected by all who were fortunate enough to know them.

—B. N.

My mom, Janice, and my dad, Donald, for unconditionally helping me pursue my seemingly impractical dreams.

My sisters, Anita and Becky, for the little ways they enrich my life.

—P. L.

We would mutually like to thank

Randy Bray, for his never-ending support and help on this book.

Joe Durepos, a great literary agent and a wonderful person as well.

Everyone at Ballantine Books who believed in this project from the very beginning.

Our Lord, Jesus Christ, who came down from heaven at Christmas and rose victorious over death at Easter.

Welcome

Christmas . . . Ask 50 different people what it means and you're likely to get a list of responses as varied as the gifts under the tree. Some might say it's the time of year when winter lays its first white blanket on a barren ground. Others will tell you it's the time when giving becomes a far greater joy than receiving. And for yet others, the season is defined by songs about mangers and a hallelujah chorus or two. While each of us may attach a meaning to Christmas peculiar to our own beliefs and desires, most of us would ultimately agree that much of Christmas's meaning is to be found in the gathering together of people, whether they be new acquaintances, old friends, or much-loved family.

It is at these Christmas gatherings, big and small, that a common little word called "conversation" takes on uncommon importance, that typical discussions of politics and careers yield a little to conversations about goodwill and great memories. We reminisce with Grandpa as logs crackle in the fireplace; we chat with our children around a freshly cut tree; we have heart-warming talks with friends at holiday dinners and share hearty laughs with colleagues around the corporate punch bowl. It would be difficult to argue that any other time of the year affords so many great opportunities to engage in conversation. With this thought in mind, *The Christmas Conversation Piece* was created.

The purpose of this book is to enhance all your Christmas conversations and draw you closer to friends and family through the use of creative and entertaining questions. Since you probably have never thought about many of the questions in this collection, you will also be drawn closer to your own thoughts, feelings, and ideas about this joyous season. Between questions about favorite carols and favorite ornaments, new gift wrapping techniques and old St. Nick, you'll never be at a loss for words. In fact, you'll find questions in here dealing with everything from tropical islands to the president of the United States—with the holiday season always at the heart of the question!

It is our hope that this book will add a new element of fun and enthusiasm to your holiday discussions while helping each one of us to rediscover Christmas, with all the enchanting nuances it has to offer. And so, from both of us, "Merry Christmas to all and to all . . . a good conversation!"

Bret Nicholaus

Paul Lowrie

1

In your opinion, what would the ultimate winter wonderland look like?

2

You're the author of a new Christmas novel that you hope will one day become a classic. What would you choose as the setting for your Christmas story?

3

What is your favorite Christmas scent?

4

What do you think is the most enjoyable thing to do in the snow?

5

If you were a photographer who was given the chance to go back in history to capture a Christmas photograph, where would you go and what year would it be?

6

Regardless of its monetary value, what is the single most meaningful Christmas gift you've ever received?

7

Someone has graciously offered to make you and your entire family a Christmas quilt. It will be made up of many quilt squares, each one representing a different family member. What specific design or image would you want on your square?

8

If time were not a concern and you had plenty of money, how would you decorate the outside of your home?

9

If, like Santa, you could take a night flight in a sleigh over any city in the world, which city would you choose?

10

Suppose that a new fad was to wrap your gifts in anything other than wrapping paper. With what would you wrap your presents?

11

What ingredients go into your favorite Christmas drink or beverage?

12

Candy canes, of course, are the traditional candy of Christmas. If you could have your way, what would be the official candy of Christmas?

13

On a scale of one to ten (with one being in perfect order and ten being an intertwined, out-of-control mess), how tangled are your Christmas lights when you first take them out each year?

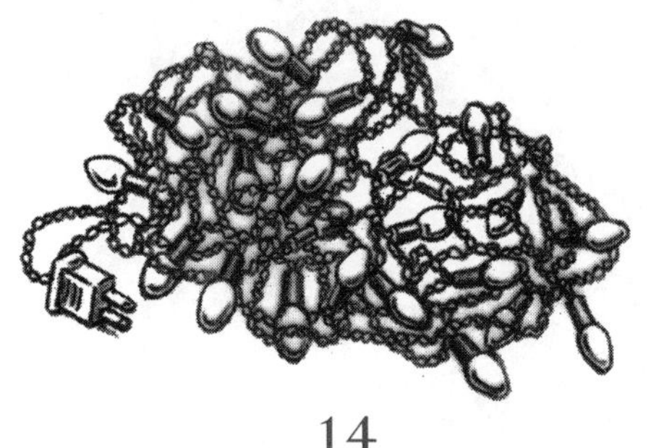

14

You've been chosen to host a sensational Christmas celebration on TV. What three guests (living or deceased) would you have on the show to make it the best Christmas special ever?

15

You have a beautiful 50-foot pine tree in your front yard that you are allowed to decorate with only one color of lights. Which color would you choose?

16

When was the last time you can remember making an angel in the snow? If it's been awhile—and you have snow—go out and do it just for fun!

17

Have you ever given someone a fruitcake for Christmas? Approximately how many fruitcakes over the years do you think you've received?

18

You are a painter and have just been commissioned to do a large oil-on-canvas painting that depicts something about the holiday season. What scene would you choose to paint?

19

If you were one of the three kings visiting the Bethlehem baby in *today's* world, what would you bring as a gift?

20

If you were designing a brand-new outfit for old St. Nick, what would it look like?

21

Which of the following three events would you most enjoy attending during the holiday season: a stage production of Dickens's *A Christmas Carol*, a choral concert of Handel's *Messiah*, or a performance of Tchaikovsky's ballet *The Nutcracker*?

22

If you could write a sequel to any Christmas movie ever produced, which one would you choose and what would the plot be?

23

If you were creating the ultimate gingerbread house, what unique features would it have?

24

In what order do you generally accessorize your tree? (Examples: Star first or last, ornaments before lights or lights before ornaments?)

25

If you could have any kind of tree besides the standard evergreen as your Christmas tree, what type would you choose?

26

What is the longest period of time you've ever left your tree up after Christmas?

27

Regardless of your gender, which role in a live nativity scene do you think you're best cut out for?

28

Suppose you have a 50-gallon aquarium in your home. How will you creatively decorate it for the fish this holiday season?

29

Of course, red and green are the traditional colors of Christmas. What two other colors do you think could—or should—become the standard for the season?

30

If you were going to be Santa Claus for a Christmas Eve, what one amenity or convenience factor would you insist that your sleigh feature?

31

What type of design or pattern on wrapping paper would definitely catch your eye?

32

You're involved in a gift exchange at work where the only thing you know about the intended recipient is that he/she is the same sex as you. Your spending cap is $15; what would you buy as the gift?

33

Do you prefer blinking or nonblinking Christmas lights?

34

Out of all the musical instruments, which one do you think is the most appropriate for the Christmas season?

35

If you had a miniature Christmas village set up in your home, what shop, building, or other object would be the most prominently displayed in your little town?

36

If you were hosting an all-expenses-paid Christmas party for children at an orphanage, what specific thing would you be sure to do to make it a Christmas the children would never forget?

37

Besides the golden rings, which gift from "The Twelve Days of Christmas" would you be most interested in receiving?

38

In your opinion, how many inches (if any) would be the ideal accumulation of snow for a white Christmas?

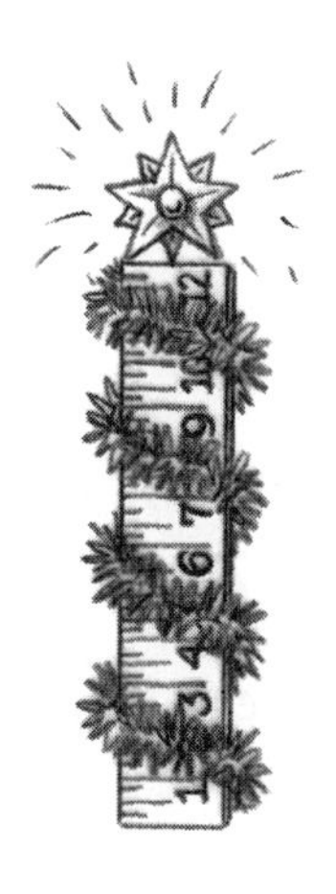

39

At Christmastime, which do you *honestly* enjoy more—giving or receiving?

40

You're in charge of developing a brand-new sport—a Christmas sport. The season begins on Thanksgiving and ends on December 25. What is your new Christmas sport going to be?

41

This year, would you rather spend Christmas at a penthouse in the city or at a cottage in the country?

42

If you were given 1,000 fresh poinsettia plants, what would you do with them? Be specific.

43

What is the first Christmas you can remember? What specific aspects of it do you recall?

44

Do you have any ethnic or ancestral traditions that you honor during the Christmas season?

45

If you had to move the celebration of Christmas from December 25 to a new date, where on the calendar would you put it?

46

In your opinion, what word(s) would best complete the following phrase: " 'Tis the season to be . . ."?

47

As the Christmas season draws near, what song is it that you can't wait to hear?

48

What particular holiday food do you enjoy the most?

49

In your opinion, what would be the ideal temperature for Christmas Day?

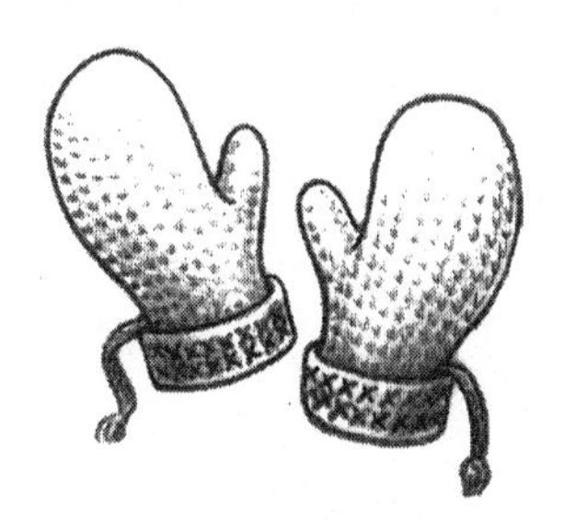

50

Without looking in your ornament storage box, approximately how many ornaments could you describe from memory?

51

Everyone at the office has been asked to place an ornament on the company Christmas tree that best represents him/herself. What would your ornament look like?

52

If you could spend Christmas in any European country, which one would you choose?

53

If you were asked to choose four songs for a Christmas medley, which songs would you pick?

54

In your opinion, how would an angelic choir look, and how would it sound? Be as specific as you can.

55

For you, what is the most discouraging aspect of the Christmas season?

56

As a curious child, did you ever shake gifts under the tree to try and figure out what you were getting? Do you still shake (or subtly lift) packages before Christmas?

57

Which particular event or aspect of the Christmas season do you look forward to most of all?

58

You must choose between Christmas caroling for a children's hospital or for a convalescent home. Which one would you choose, and what reason would you give to defend your choice?

59

If you had written the story, what type of animal would be pulling Santa's sleigh?

60

What is your favorite Christmas sound?

61

If you won $5,000 the week before Christmas, where do you think you'd go for a Christmas vacation?

62

This year, what is the most important thing on your Christmas list?

63

If you own a pet, does it have its own stocking? Does it get Christmas gifts along with everyone else?

64

If snow could fall in any flavor, what flavor would you choose?

65

If an ice company offered to carve a large ice sculpture for you, what object would you want them to carve?

66

What makes a Christmas gift really special to you?

67

If you could somehow give one of the following intangible gifts to every person living in the world, which one would you choose—hope, joy, love, or peace?

68

If you were creating a movie about toys coming to life, which toy would be your main character?

69

What is the longest line you can remember waiting in during the Christmas season?

70

If you were given thousands of dollars to develop an incredible electric train layout that would run at the base of a huge Christmas tree in a mall, what might it look like upon completion?

71

Approximately how many parties do you attend during the typical Christmas season?

72

If you had outstanding promotion and distribution working behind you, what brand-new toy—children's or adults'—would you create and introduce?

73

What is the oldest ornament on your Christmas tree?

74

Where does Santa summer?

75

If you could Christmas shop until you drop in any one store, which store would you choose?

76

When does it *really* start feeling like Christmas to you?

77

In terms of overall size, how large (or small) do you envision Santa's workshop?

78

When you think of the holiday season in New York City, what particular scene or image do you picture first?

79

If you were in charge of hiring a department store Santa, what quality or ability above all others would you look for in the applicants?

80

In which of the following locations would you most enjoy spending Christmas—Colorado, Tennessee, or Vermont?

81

If you were going to go out for dinner on Christmas Day, would you tip more than usual since the waiter or waitress is having to work on the holiday?

82

How many people do you know named Joseph? How many people do you know named Mary?

83

Were you ever in a Christmas pageant? If so, what part did you play?

84

According to the biblical Christmas story, Mary was very surprised to learn that she would be bearing the son of God. What is the best Christmas surprise that you've ever had?

85

Everyone has a favorite Christmas story or experience that he/she loves to share. What's yours?

86

If you had the money to develop the ultimate fireplace, what would it look like?

87

How many new words can you derive from the word *Christmas*? You need not use all the letters. (Example: The word *his*.)

88

Do you have a traditional Christmas dinner that you prepare year after year? If so, what is it?

89

How do you think you would react if *you* were visited by an angel?

90

If, as the winner of a Christmas contest, you were given five minutes in one of the following three departments to haul away as many items as you could physically carry out the door, which department would you choose—consumer electronics, home furnishings and accessories, or sports equipment and attire? (Assume that you cannot solicit the help of a salesperson.)

91

If you were hosting a small group of people for a Christmas party and had to choose something other than showing a movie for the entertainment, what would you choose?

92

Approximately how many Christmas cards do you send out each year?

93

Have you ever cut down your own Christmas tree? If you had a convenient opportunity to do so, would you?

94

In terms of height, shape, and type, what would you consider the ideal Christmas tree?

95

What do you typically do the day after Christmas?

96

If an acquaintance wanted to spend about $15 on a gift for you, what would you suggest that he/she buy?

97

If you could dress up a snowman as someone famous, who would it look like?

98

It's a *Wonderful Life*, *Miracle on 34th Street*, or *White Christmas*—which one would get your vote for the best classic Christmas movie?

99

If you had a child born on Christmas Day and had to give him/her a name that related to Christmas, what name would you choose? (Example: *Holly* for a girl.)

100

If you were going to create and market a holiday cologne or perfume, what would you choose for the fragrance?

101

Given the choice, would you rather host people at your place for Christmas or travel and spend the holiday at someone else's home?

102

If you could indulge in only one type of cookie this holiday season, which cookie would you be eating a lot of?

103

If, through the use of a time machine, you could travel back in time to briefly revisit any Christmas moment in your life, which one would you choose?

104

If you had to write a Christmas greeting no more than ten words in length that would be printed on 100,000 Christmas cards, what would it be?

105

A large snowman has been built in a popular city park; it is your job to supply the hat for his head. What hat would you choose to make this snowman unique?

106

Approximately how many dozens of cookies do you bake during a typical Christmas season? Would you like to guess at how many you eat during the season?

107

If you could go anywhere at all to reflect and meditate on the meaning of Christmas, where would you go?

108

What has been your worst holiday travel dilemma/experience to date?

109

What gift have you wanted for years, but still haven't received?

110

In your opinion, what is the most timeless toy?

111

What's the most creative way you can think of to decorate your car for Christmas?

112

When does your family traditionally open gifts?

113

If you could decorate any store's window for the Christmas season, which one would you choose?

114

Many snow globes feature something other than snow that falls (e.g., hundreds of little, white bones in a globe featuring a dog). What do you think would be most interesting to have falling inside a snow globe?

115

What is your all-time biggest Christmas shopping disaster?

116

Suppose that a friend or relative gives you a gift that he/she is personally very excited to have given. You, on the other hand, either have no use for it or simply don't like it. How would you react to the giver? Would you pretend that you like it? Would you try to exchange it for cash or for another item?

117

If you could invite any famous person to your house for Christmas dinner, whom would you invite?

118

If you could have two front-row tickets for any musical event this Christmas, what or whom would you most like to hear?

119

Of all your friends and family members, which person do you think is best suited to play the part of Santa Claus?

120

If you were to file a complaint with the Better Christmas Bureau, what would your complaint be?

121

If you were playing Name That Tune, which Christmas song do you think you could identify in the least number of notes? Think carefully!

122

If someone wanted to give you a $100 gift certificate for Christmas, what store would you want it to be from?

123

If you could go back in American history to experience Christmas dinner and conversation with a typical family of that day, which of the following years would you want to go back to?

a. 1620, the year the *Mayflower* arrived
b. 1787, the year the Constitution was signed
c. 1863, midway through the American Civil War
d. 1899, the turn of the century

124

If you were to open up a cozy, little Christmas shop, what Christmas product would be your main draw?

125

If you were the coordinator in charge of staging a nationwide Christmas event, one in which every American theoretically could participate, what would this grand event be?

126

A candy cane company, which lost sales last year to the chocolate market, has asked you to create a catchy slogan that positions candy canes as the superior candy. What will your slogan be? Take a few minutes and have some fun with this one!

127

What aspect of preparing for Christmas do you like the most?

128

Suppose that a major motion-picture company was producing a Christmas movie about a real-life Grinch. What actor or actress do you think would be best suited to play the leading role?

129

By the time Christmas actually arrives, many of us are too tired to enjoy it. Approximately when—between Thanksgiving and December 25—does your holiday spirit peak?

130

Suppose you could have any gift in the world this Christmas, regardless of cost, provided it could fit in the trunk of a mid-sized car. What would you want?

131

Have you ever worked in retail sales during the holiday season? If so, what was your most interesting experience?

132

Suppose that there was a nationwide shortage of Christmas trees and prices went through the roof. Assuming that artificial trees are not an option, what is the absolute most you'd be willing to pay for a real tree?

133

If you were going to write an editorial column for your city's newspaper covering any Christmas topic of your choice, what would you write about?

134

If you could create the perfect hill for sledding, what would it look like? Be specific.

135

If Frosty the Snowman really did come to life for a day, what one national attraction or tourist site would you encourage him to see before he melted away?

136

No other time of the year affords such a great opportunity to enjoy good food and drink. In your opinion, what is the best taste the Christmas season has to offer?

137

A major theme of the Christmas season is peace on earth. For whatever your reason, what do you consider the most peaceful place on earth?

138

What aspect of preparing for Christmas do you like the least?

139

What would you choose as an international symbol for the word *Christmas*?

140

What is your favorite Christmas phrase, quote, or verse?

141

If you were the one delivering gifts to all the world's children, what would you consider the perfect temperature for your all-night sleigh flight around the earth?

142

How likely are you to run out of wrapping paper before you finish wrapping all your gifts? Do you have a lot of leftover paper at the end of the season?

143

If luck favored you and you won $100,000 during the holiday season, what percent of your winnings (if any) do you think you'd give away to others?

144

What is your favorite Christmas decoration in your home? (The Christmas tree doesn't count!)

145

If you were a movie producer, which of the following three cities would you choose as the setting for a new Christmas movie—New York, Denver, or Minneapolis?

146

Whose televised Christmas special do you anticipate the most each year?

147

If it were socially acceptable for you to play with any children's toy, with which toy would you be spending a lot of time?

148

If you were blind, but miraculously had the chance to see for 24 hours during one holiday of the year, would you necessarily choose Christmas? If not, which holiday would you most want to see?

149

If you could de-commercialize Christmas, what is the first change you would make?

150

At what age do you think children are the cutest to watch at Christmas?

151

Which state in our country do you find the most difficult to associate with the Christmas season?

152

Each year Easter falls at a slightly different time on the calendar. How would you feel if Christmas followed a similar pattern, falling at a different time each year between Thanksgiving and New Year's?

153

If you were in charge of developing a town that would be the most peaceful place to live on earth, which particular features would characterize it?

154

Have you ever purposely stood under mistletoe with the hope of being kissed by someone? Have you ever unknowingly stood under mistletoe and been kissed by someone?

155

For the perfect romantic evening during the holiday season, where would you most want to go?

156

Regardless of the electric bill, what man-made or natural object would you most like to see strung or outlined with Christmas lights?

157

During the Christmas season, would you be more likely to give money to a certain charity or to a specific individual in need?

158

What magazine and/or catalog's Christmas issue is an absolute "must read" for you?

159

What would be the ideal way for you to spend Christmas Eve?

160

If any Christmas song were to bring you to tears, which one would it be?

161

If you had to ascribe an age to Santa Claus based on how old you think he looks, what age would you give him?

162

Suppose you have just arrived from another planet and are getting your first glimpse of this thing called Christmas. Having never heard of Christmas or experienced it in any way, what do you think you would find most fascinating about it?

163

According to the biblical Christmas story, the three kings followed a star and ultimately found the baby Jesus. What is the greatest thing, tangible or intangible, that *you've* ever found?

164

Which of the following, if it were completely and permanently removed from the holiday season, would be the most difficult for you to get along without—Christmas lights, Christmas music, or Christmas parties? Think carefully!

165

If you were asked to concoct a Christmas dessert for a five-star restaurant, what would the dessert be?

166

If you were on a committee assigned to decorating the world's largest Christmas tree, what suggestions would you have for the adorning of the tree?

167

What is one Christmas tradition that you have not yet started but that you think would be fun to begin?

168

What Christmas object in your home has the most sentimental value?

169

What Christmas song drives you nuts?

170

If you had the opportunity to take a Christmas ride down and around Chicago's famous Michigan Avenue, would you rather take the tour in one of the popular horse-drawn carriages or in a luxurious white stretch limousine?

171

During the holiday season, what specific aspect of being a young child do you miss the most?

172

Have you ever kept track of how much money you spend in one year directly related to Christmas (e.g., gifts, entertaining, and the like)?

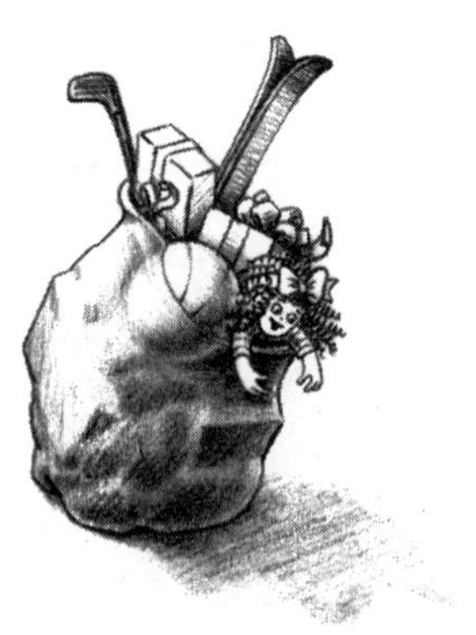

173

What is one of the simple joys of Christmas that you like to savor to the fullest?

174

If you had a great voice and could record a Christmas duet with any famous singer, whom would you choose as your singing partner?

175

What is your favorite holiday of the entire year?

176

For the sake of comparison, you've been asked to stage two scenes of the American family and household at Christmas—one scene is this year, the other scene is 30 years ago. What differences would people see between the two? Be specific.

177

On a scale of one to ten (with one being very relaxing and ten being very stressful), how stressful is the holiday season for you?

178

If you could somehow change the number of days in the month of December, would you make the month longer or shorter, and by how many days?

179

If you were Santa Claus, what food and beverage would you want children to leave for you?

180

If you could get anyone in the world to be the keynote speaker for a large Christmas dinner you're coordinating, whom would you choose?

181

If you were one of three judges in charge of selecting the best small-town Christmas in the United States, what particular criterion would be most important in your decision?

182

If you were involved in a progressive holiday dinner, for which course would you want to be responsible—hors d'oeuvres, soup, salad, main course, or dessert?

183

Do you ever listen to Christmas music out of season (e.g., in the middle of summer)?

184

If keeping the laughs going at your Christmas party was a primary concern, whom would you be sure to invite out of all your friends?

185

If you were asked to write a dictionary definition for the word *Christmas*, how would you define it in 20 words or less?

186

If you could have any Christmas antique, what would you choose?

187

If you could somehow "jump into" any Christmas carol or song and actually experience what the lyrics say, which song would you choose?

188

If you were the owner of a bed-and-breakfast inn, what would you do to make the Christmas season special for your guests?

189

What is one thing you've always wanted to do during the holiday season, but haven't done thus far?

190

If you were going to establish a U.S. mailing address for Santa Claus, which city and state do you think would be most appropriate?

191

During the rush of the Christmas season, which chore, activity, or discipline do you tend to neglect the most?

192

If you were to receive a tin of all the same kind of nut, would you want it to contain cashews, filberts, pecans, or pistachios?

193

If you could make a wish upon a Christmas star, what would you wish for?

194

You're in charge of developing a planned community called Christmas City. What are some of the plans on the drawing board that keep with the Christmas theme?

195

If you could spend Christmas Day with any TV family, past or present, with which family would you choose to celebrate? (Example: The Bunkers.)

196

If Christmas is a state of mind, what attitude or attribute above all others need one possess in order to maintain a Christmas state of mind all year long?

197

Which winter/holiday Currier and Ives print comes to your mind first?

198

Other than simply giving a small check or cash gift, what act of kindness do you think would be nice to do for an individual in need this Christmas season?

199

Besides the reindeer, which animal(s) do you associate the most with the Christmas season?

200

You have two options for where you can spend Christmas: a ski resort in the mountains or a tropical resort on a Caribbean island. Which would you choose?

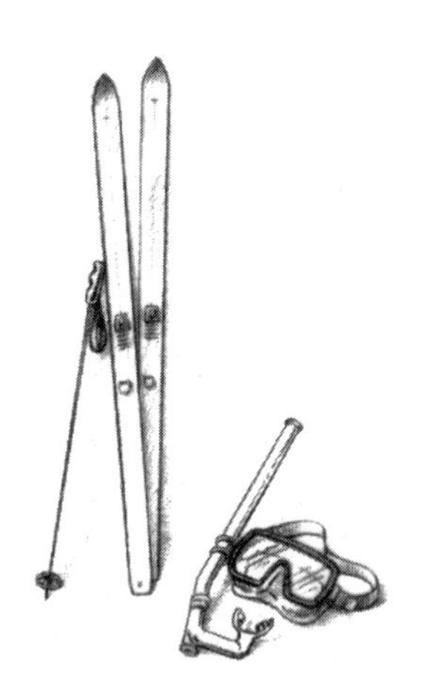

201

If you or your family could have a Christmas photograph taken anywhere in the world, where would you want to have the picture taken? (Assume the photo will be sent out in all your Christmas cards.)

202

If you were the wedding coordinator in charge of a Christmas wedding, what is one Christmas detail that you would want to incorporate into the big day?

203

If you had to replace the customary Christmas tree with a new Christmas conversation piece, what would become its replacement?

204

If a baker offered to bake you one specific treat for Christmas, what would you choose?

205

If this Christmas you could be instantly transported to London's St. Paul's Cathedral to hear any one musical work or composition, what would you most want to hear? (It needn't have a Christmas theme.)

206

How long before Christmas do you traditionally begin shopping for gifts?

207

If you were president of the United States, what nonmonetary act of goodwill would you want the country to see you performing?

208

If you could take a how-to course in anything related to the Christmas season, in what course would you want to enroll?

209

If you got a puppy or kitten for Christmas and had to name it after one of the nine reindeer—Dasher, Dancer, Prancer, Vixen, Comet, Cupid, Donner, Blitzen, or Rudolph—what would you name it?

210

He's making a list and checking it twice. On a scale of one to ten (with one being very naughty and ten being very nice), how naughty or nice have you been this year?

211

There are two gifts under the tree with your name on them, but you may only choose one. One gift is in a three-inch-square box, the other is in a three-foot-square box. The monetary value of both gifts is exactly the same; which one will you choose? (No fair shaking!)

212

Take a few moments and paint a picture of the word *December* in your mind's eye. What does it look like? Describe it vividly!

213

In that famous Christmas song, all the child wants is his two front teeth. If you could receive any physical feature or attribute this Christmas, what would you ask for?

214

What is the most unusual and/or unique Christmas tradition you've ever heard of?

215

Which particular job would you least like to have around the holiday season?

216

In how many different languages can you say "Merry Christmas"?

217

If you could see one snowfall in a color other than white, what color would you want it to be?

218

If you were going to make a Christmas wreath out of something other than pine boughs, what would you use to make your wreath truly unique?

219

Around Christmastime there really does seem to be a special feeling in the air. What particular feeling above all others does Christmas evoke in you?

220

In that famous Christmas poem, the house is so quiet the night before Christmas that not even a mouse is stirring. What is the usual atmosphere in your house the night before Christmas?

221

If you could decorate any famous building for Christmas (inside and outside), which building would you choose?

222

What's your favorite holiday commercial or advertisement?

223

If any of our past presidents—living or deceased—could be brought back for a day to deliver a Christmas address to the nation, whose speech would you be most interested in hearing?

224

If a child asked you what causes Rudolph's nose to glow, what would your response be?

225

As a late-night talk-show host, you must book a guest for your December 23 show who is highly relevant to the Christmas season. Whom would you choose as the guest? (The person does not have to be famous.)

226

Which Christmas song's lyrics have you memorized more completely than any other?

227

If you were to start a snow globe collection around a certain theme, what would the theme be?

228

What Christmas object(s) do you think would be the most eye-catching if it were printed on a tie?

229

Are you more likely to give someone a gift that they really *want* or a gift that you think they really *need*?

230

Which of the following three holidays do you enjoy the most, and which do you enjoy the least—Thanksgiving Day, Christmas Day, or New Year's Day?

231

If you were going to create and market an ice cream especially for the Christmas season, what would it be like?

232

If you had to describe your personality in terms of a Christmas object, which object would you choose? (Example: A snow globe, if you're the type who gets "shaken up" easily.)

233

If you could walk down a path that would lead you into an experience of perfect Christmas joy and bliss, to what specific experience would you most want to be led?

234

If you could create a new holiday by blending Christmas traditions with those of another established holiday, which two special days would you combine?

235

If you were going to decorate a Christmas tree outdoors for the birds and animals, what type of edibles would you hang from the tree?

236

How many words beginning with the letter *C* can you think of that relate directly to the Christmas season? (Example: Candle.)

237

If you were given one pound of fresh cranberries, what would you do with them?

238

Which job or occupation do you think would be the most rewarding around the holiday season?

239

In your opinion, do the large crowds of people at Christmastime add or detract from the overall shopping experience?

240

When the excitement of Christmas and New Year's is over, what is the next big day that you begin to anticipate?

241

What is the most creative way you can think of to present an engagement ring during the holidays?

242

If all the Christmas gifts you gave away this year had to be homemade by you, what would you be most likely to make?

243

What is the most interesting piece of Christmas trivia that you know?

244

You must add a new pair of reindeer to Santa's sleigh-pulling team (the load's a little heavier this year). What would you name the two newcomers?

245

Have you ever written clues on gift tags to give the recipient "a sneak preview" as to what's inside? (Example: "This gift serves you right," if you're giving a tennis racket.)

246

What street in your city or town do you most like to walk down during the Christmas season?

247

What has been the greatest blessing in your life since last Christmas?

248

Do you know who Clement Clarke Moore was?

249

What Christmas movie that you haven't seen for years are you yearning to see again?

250

Which particular aspect of the biblical Christmas account are you most interested in?

251

If fallen snow had a scent, what scent would you want it to have?

252

Which particular person that you've lost contact with would you most like to surprise with a phone call this Christmas?

253

What is the greatest extreme you've ever gone to in order to get someone a particular Christmas gift?

254

If you could take a scenic drive anywhere in America this holiday season, where would you most want to drive?

255

In the song "The Twelve Days of Christmas," how many gifts would one receive if you added up all of the gifts given in every verse from day one to day twelve?

256

What is your best explanation for children of how Santa can fit down a chimney? What if there is no chimney?

257

You, your family, and your friends are trapped in your home for three days following a Christmas Eve blizzard. What would you do to keep everyone entertained and retain a sense of peace in the house?

258

If you were caught in the act of opening one of your Christmas presents before Christmas, what excuse would you be likely to give?

259

What's the best use you can think of for snow?

260

Suppose you were the cruise director for a riverboat making a Christmas cruise down the Mississippi River. What would you do to make this four-hour dinner cruise a Christmas event that all the passengers would remember?

261

Suppose you were one of ten individuals randomly selected to do some Christmas caroling. On a scale of one to ten (with one being the best singer and ten being the worst), how do you think your singing ability would rank relative to the other people in the group?

262

If you were going to create your own greeting cards this holiday season, what would you do to make them unique?

263

If you were an airline pilot with a plane full of passengers at 12:00 A.M. on Christmas Day, what might you do (or have your crew do) to make the arrival of Christmas Day special?

264

If you could cover any large area with ice *besides* a body of water, what would you want to ice over?

265

When was the last time you decorated a Christmas tree on Christmas Eve?

266

If you could decorate a tree in your house for another holiday besides Christmas, what holiday would it be?

267

If you made music boxes for your living, what one really unique box would you introduce for this Christmas season?

268

What is one thing you will do this Christmas that you were unable to do or attend last Christmas?

269

If you had to miss your family's Christmas celebration (such as hanging the stockings, Christmas dinner, opening gifts, trimming the tree, etc.), which part would you miss the most?

270

Would you rather receive a puppy or a kitten as a Christmas gift?

271

Have you ever secretly communicated your Christmas gift preference to someone? How did you do it?

272

If you were the president of a large corporation and could give only one type of gift to your 1,000 employees, what would it be?

273

If you could hire a skywriter to write a special Christmas message in the sky over your city or town, what would it be?

274

What's the greatest distance you've ever traveled in order to take part in a Christmas celebration?

275

If you kept a journal of Christmases, which year's Christmas would have the lengthiest entry?

276

Have you ever begun a friendship or romance with someone on Christmas?

277

Have you ever opened someone else's present by mistake?

278

What color do you think Santa's hair was before it turned white?

279

Have you ever written a letter to Santa? Did you get an answer back?

280

What's your favorite day of the week for Christmas to fall on?

281

Who is the oldest person you've ever celebrated Christmas with?

282

What room in your house has the least number of decorations at Christmas?

283

Once Christmas has come and gone, are you the type that wants spring to arrive as fast as possible?

284

You're the editor of a general-interest magazine. What will you put on the cover of your Christmas issue?

285

What movie's Christmas celebration would you most like to have attended?

286

What's your preferred method of displaying Christmas cards, if you display them at all?

287

If you had to receive the same gift each year, what would you want it to be?

288

If you had to give the same gift to every person on your Christmas list, what would it be?

289

What's the largest Christmas Day (or Christmas Eve) gathering you've ever attended?

290

What's the first Christmas song you remember learning?

291

If you were a department store Santa, which aspects of the job would you enjoy the most?

292

What's the biggest change in your life since last Christmas?

293

If money were no object, would you hire a personal shopper to do your Christmas shopping for you?

294

Have you ever “recycled” a Christmas gift?

295

If you could receive any new Christmas ornament this holiday season, what would you like it to be?

296

Have you ever had a present destroyed by an inquisitive (or hungry) pet?

297

What's the warmest Christmas you can remember?

298

In your opinion, what would the ideal centerpiece look like for a holiday dinner in your home? Describe it in detail.

299

What do you do with your Christmas cards after the holidays are over?

300

If snow could somehow fall and accumulate in a warm climate, would you enjoy it more?

301

As the end of the year approaches, it's only natural to reflect back on the last twelve months. Which three news events would you label as the most memorable of the year?

302

If you were hosting a Christmas party and had to choose one question in this book to use as an icebreaker with your guests, which one would you choose?

A Note to Our Readers

Many of you have shared with us the creative ways you've found to use our books: in school classrooms; at dinner parties; in college dormitories; at family gatherings; at reunions; and during coffee breaks with friends or coworkers. We've even heard from folks who have found the books especially fun and entertaining on long car trips and when traveling by plane.

Please let us know how *you* are enjoying the books; we would love to hear from you. Write to us at the address below, and thank you for including us in your conversations!

Bret Nicholaus & Paul Lowrie
P.O. Box 340
Yankton, SD 57078

About the Authors

Bret Nicholaus and Paul Lowrie are 1991 graduates of Bethel College, St. Paul, Minnesota. They hold degrees in public relations/advertising and marketing, respectively. Both authors firmly believe that creative questioning is the key to learning about ourselves and others. They are the authors of the bestselling *The Conversation Piece*, *The Christmas Conversation Piece*, and *The Mom & Dad Conversation Piece*.